INSIDE...

SUPER SOLDIER!

Transformed from a ten-pound weakling into a muscle-bound titan by an experimental serum, Steve Rogers was America's greatest hero during World War 2. As their secret weapon, Cap spent most of the war fighting the Nazis in Europe and protecting his own country.

His suit is completely bulletproof.

A HEROIC SACRIFICE!

But tragedy struck in 1945 when Cap was seemingly killed trying to defuse an experimental drone plane created by the evil Baron Zemo. The plane exploded over the North Atlantic Ocean, sending Cap's body plunging into the icy seas below.

Captain America can lift up to a maximum of 800 pounds.

RETURN OF A LEGEND!

Somehow, the serum in his blood kept Captain America in a state of perfect hibernation. Years later he was found by the Avengers frozen in a block of ice. After being thawed out, he was invited to join the group, and eventually became their new leader.

Cap can run a mile in just over one minute.

BATTLE TACTICS!

Cap's shield is his trademark weapon. It is made from an alloy of steel and the energy absorbing metal vibranium, and is virtually indestructible.

He can use his shield to take down multiple opponents at once by throwing it in such a way that it will bounce from enemy to enemy, and then return to his hand like a boomerang.

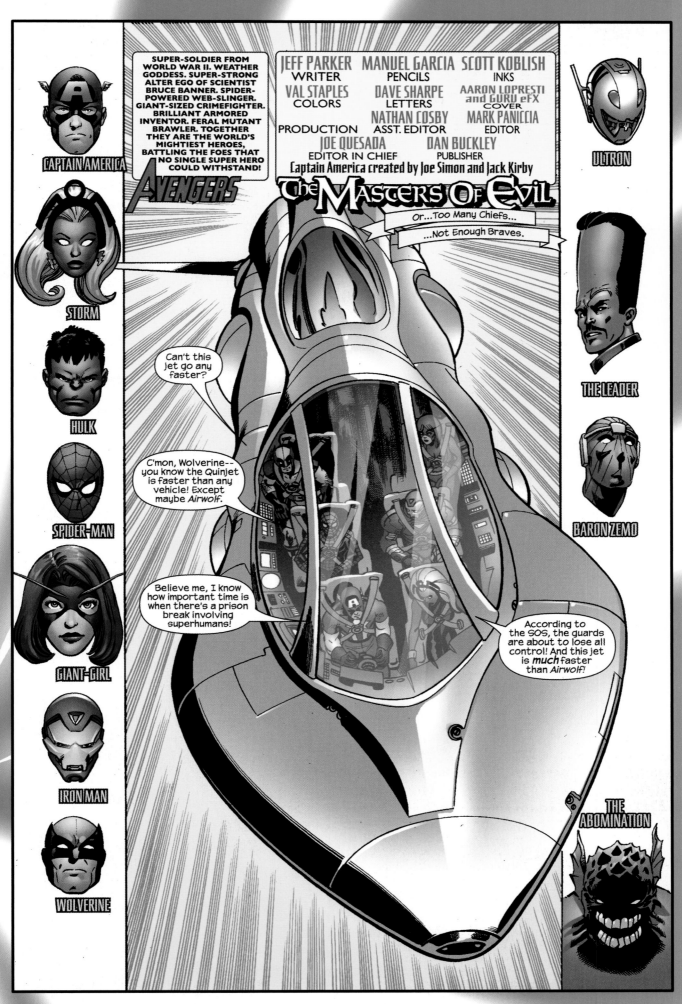

CAPTAIN AMERICA

STORM

HULK

SPIDER-MAN

GIANT-GIRL

IRON MAN

WOLVERINE

SUPER-SOLDIER FROM WORLD WAR II. WEATHER GODDESS. SUPER-STRONG ALTER EGO OF SCIENTIST BRUCE BANNER. SPIDER-POWERED WEB-SLINGER. GIANT-SIZED CRIMEFIGHTER. BRILLIANT ARMORED INVENTOR. FERAL MUTANT BRAWLER. TOGETHER THEY ARE THE WORLD'S MIGHTIEST HEROES, BATTLING THE FOES THAT NO SINGLE SUPER HERO COULD WITHSTAND!

AVENGERS

JEFF PARKER
WRITER

MANUEL GARCIA
PENCILS

SCOTT KOBLISH
INKS

VAL STAPLES
COLORS

DAVE SHARPE
LETTERS

AARON LOPRESTI and GURU eFX
COVER

NATHAN COSBY
ASST. EDITOR

MARK PANICCIA
EDITOR

PRODUCTION

JOE QUESADA
EDITOR IN CHIEF

DAN BUCKLEY
PUBLISHER

Captain America created by Joe Simon and Jack Kirby

THE MASTERS OF EVIL

Or...Too Many Chiefs...

...Not Enough Braves.

Can't this jet go any faster?

C'mon, Wolverine-- you know the Quinjet is faster than any vehicle! Except maybe Airwolf.

Believe me, I know how important time is when there's a prison break involving superhumans!

According to the SOS, the guards are about to lose all control! And this jet is much faster than Airwolf!

ULTRON

THE LEADER

BARON ZEMO

THE ABOMINATION

AVENGERS ROLLCALL!

FILE #02

Check it out, True Believers! Get ready for some serious fire power as we lift the lid on one of the world's most hi-tech heroes, Iron Man!

> He can lift over 70 tons.

> Iron Man can fly at speeds of up to 960 mph.

— CAPTURED! —

Whilst field testing a new weapon created by his company Stark Industries, billionaire business man Tony Stark was kidnapped by a terrorist cell. Imprisoned in their camp, he was told that he would only be released if he built an advanced weapon for them.

— A DARING ESCAPE! —

Stark agreed, but instead of building a weapon he secretly created a hi-tech armoured suit. He used the experimental suit to blast his way out of the camp and escape from his captors.

— ARMOURED HERO! —

Returning to America, Tony realised that he could use his incredible mechanical armour to protect people from super powered threats. He redesigned his suit, greatly improving on his original design. After years of creating weapons of war, Tony could now be a force for good, saving people from harm as Iron Man.

⚡ BATTLE TACTICS!

His most powerful weapon is the Unibeam Projector built into his chest. Using this he can project different blasts of energy at his opponents such as hard radiation, gravity waves and plasma beams.

The repulsor beams built into his gloves are strong enough to blast a hole straight through a 3 foot thick block of concrete.

Iron Man's armour is covered in a special paint that makes it completely invisible to radar.

AVENGERS ROLLCALL!

FILE #03

WOLVERINE

With his razor sharp claws and short temper, Wolverine is one of the most dangerous heroes in the Marvel Universe. Read on to discover why he's the best there is at what he does!

His claws are sharp enough to cut through any armour.

Thanks to his enhanced senses, Wolverine can sniff out an opponent from up to a mile away.

— WEAPON X! —

Years ago, Wolverine was forced to become a test subject for a military organisation known as Weapon X. In their attempt to create a new super soldier, they bonded the indestructible metal adamantium to his bones. Though the process would've killed a normal man, Wolverine survived the operation thanks to his mutant healing ability.

— FREEDOM! —

Though he was driven half mad by the procedure, he somehow managed to escape the Weapon X facility. He was found by a couple called James and Heather Macdonald who nursed him back to health. Once he had recovered from his ordeal, Wolverine was offered a place on the Canadian Super Hero team Alpha Flight. He turned them down, opting to join Professor Xavier's team of mutant heroes, the X-Men, instead.

— CLAWS OF RAGE! —

Wolverine is an exceptional fighter, but can be overcome by a berserker rage when he is under extreme pressure in combat. The Avengers know to treat him with extreme caution when this happens, as he will lash out at the nearest target regardless of whether they are friend or foe.

BATTLE TACTICS!

He is an expert at hand-to-hand combat and has an extensive knowledge of nearly all forms of martial arts.

His greatest asset is his healing factor. Within a couple of minutes he can fully recover from an injury that would kill a normal man.

It is believed that Wolverine is over 100 years old, however this can't be proved as his healing factor covers up any sign of ageing.

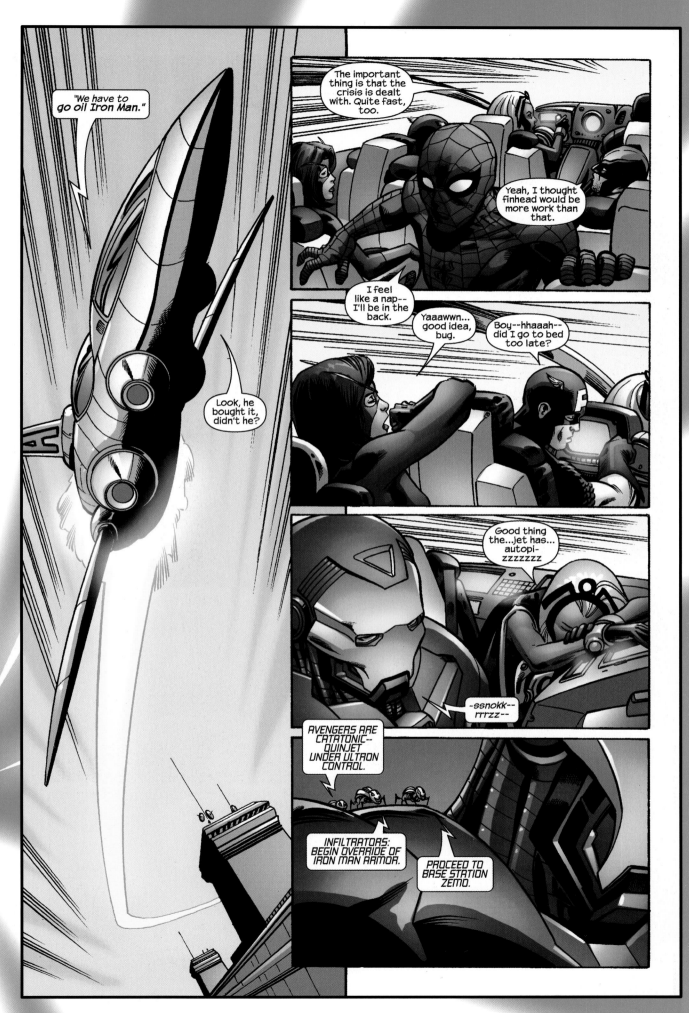

Grrrrrr...

Wolverine, of course, could slice through the walls, but I somehow doubt he'll wish to project his claws.

MUTANT STORM'S CELL INHIBITS HER INFLUENCE OVER BAROMETRIC PRESSURE AND IONIC FIELDS, RENDERING HER POWERLESS.

THE ULTRON SYSTEM HAS ALSO OVERRIDDEN THE CONTROL CORE OF THE IRON MAN ARMOR, RENDERING IT UNUSABLE BY THE WEARER.

If...I could just move...my fingers...

Ultron, Ultron. You need to really work on gloating.

Factually stating how a hero is defeated is nice, but draw it out a bit...rub it in!

THE AVENGERS CANNOT FUNCTION AT PEAK PROFICIENCY.

Um... a little better.

I just realized...

VOLCANO IS UNSTABLE. ULTRON RECOMMENDS NEW COMMAND LOCATION.

ULTRON ALSO RECOMMENDS AVENGERS BE DESTROYED IMMEDIATELY.

Oh, Ultron, you'd have us based out of an office park. Humanity regards us as nothing less than Masters of Evil! A volcano base gives the proper sense of daring and flair! Excellent choice, Baron.

Well, I had a volcano going unused. It simply seemed--

THEN ULTRON SUGGESTS DESTRUCTION OF THE AVENGERS WILL MEET THE LEADER'S AGENDA OF DARING AND FLAIR.

Absolutely not! Not all of them, anyway.

The Hulk has a weak brain that I could override. His brute strength would add to our forces immensely.

I like the destroy-Captain-America part of your suggestion.

ULTRON HAD NOT CONSIDERED ALTERING ALLEGIANCES OF THE HEROES. THE IRON MAN ARMOR IS ALREADY UNDER ULTRON CONTROL.

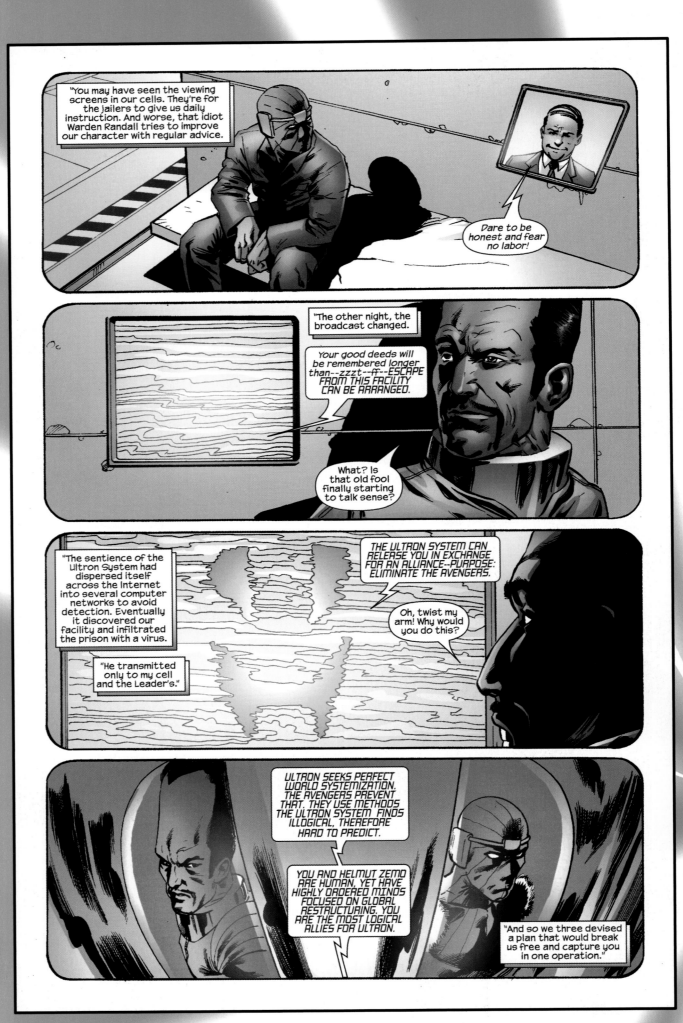

"You may have seen the viewing screens in our cells. They're for the jailers to give us daily instruction. And worse, that idiot Warden Randall tries to improve our character with regular advice.

Dare to be honest and fear no labor!

"The other night, the broadcast changed.

Your good deeds will be remembered longer than--zzzt--ff--ESCAPE FROM THIS FACILITY CAN BE ARRANGED.

What? Is that old fool finally starting to talk sense?

"The sentience of the Ultron System had dispersed itself across the Internet into several computer networks to avoid detection. Eventually it discovered our facility and infiltrated the prison with a virus.

"He transmitted only to my cell and the Leader's."

THE ULTRON SYSTEM CAN RELEASE YOU IN EXCHANGE FOR AN ALLIANCE--PURPOSE: ELIMINATE THE AVENGERS.

Oh, twist my arm! Why would you do this?

ULTRON SEEKS PERFECT WORLD SYSTEMIZATION. THE AVENGERS PREVENT THAT. THEY USE METHODS THE ULTRON SYSTEM FINDS ILLOGICAL, THEREFORE HARD TO PREDICT.

YOU AND HELMUT ZEMO ARE HUMAN, YET HAVE HIGHLY ORDERED MINDS FOCUSED ON GLOBAL RESTRUCTURING. YOU ARE THE MOST LOGICAL ALLIES FOR ULTRON.

"And so we three devised a plan that would break us free and capture you in one operation."

SPIDER-MAN
Hey guys! Next up is your friendly neighbourhood Spider-Man! Read on to discover all his secrets!

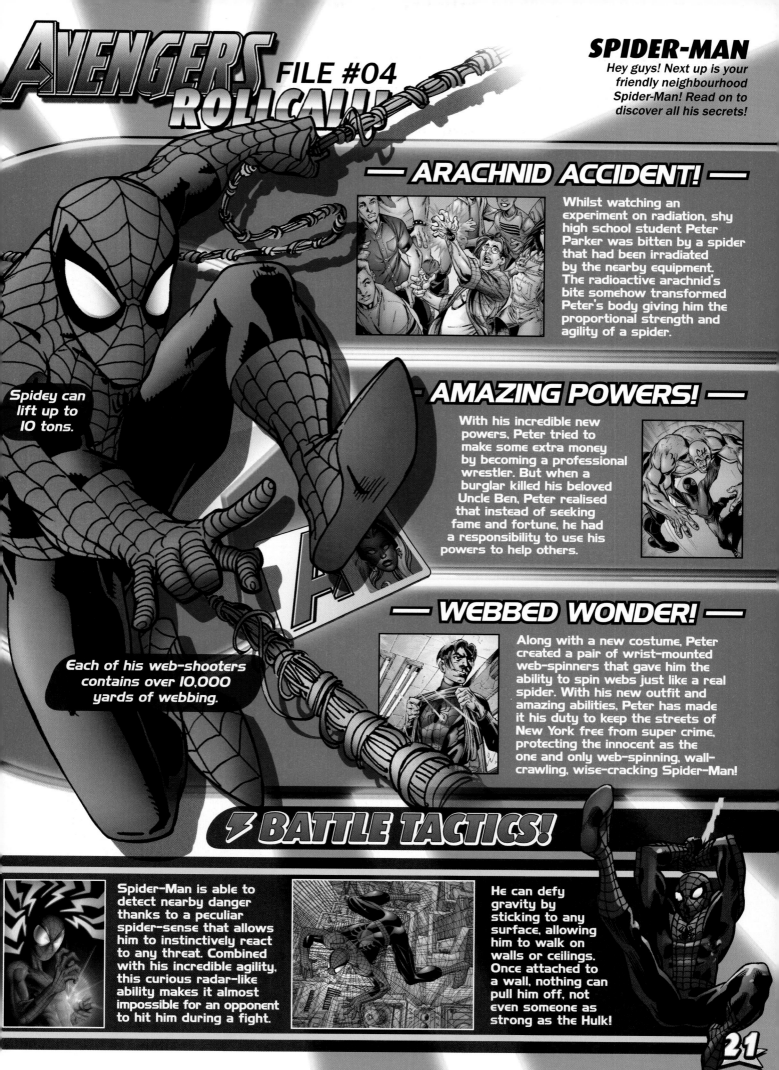

— ARACHNID ACCIDENT! —

Whilst watching an experiment on radiation, shy high school student Peter Parker was bitten by a spider that had been irradiated by the nearby equipment. The radioactive arachnid's bite somehow transformed Peter's body giving him the proportional strength and agility of a spider.

Spidey can lift up to 10 tons.

— AMAZING POWERS! —

With his incredible new powers, Peter tried to make some extra money by becoming a professional wrestler. But when a burglar killed his beloved Uncle Ben, Peter realised that instead of seeking fame and fortune, he had a responsibility to use his powers to help others.

Each of his web-shooters contains over 10,000 yards of webbing.

— WEBBED WONDER! —

Along with a new costume, Peter created a pair of wrist-mounted web-spinners that gave him the ability to spin webs just like a real spider. With his new outfit and amazing abilities, Peter has made it his duty to keep the streets of New York free from super crime, protecting the innocent as the one and only web-spinning, wall-crawling, wise-cracking Spider-Man!

⚡ BATTLE TACTICS!

Spider-Man is able to detect nearby danger thanks to a peculiar spider-sense that allows him to instinctively react to any threat. Combined with his incredible agility, this curious radar-like ability makes it almost impossible for an opponent to hit him during a fight.

He can defy gravity by sticking to any surface, allowing him to walk on walls or ceilings. Once attached to a wall, nothing can pull him off, not even someone as strong as the Hulk!

GIANT GIRL

Hey guys. Here's one Super Hero who's got no problem going super sized. Take a look below to find out all about her!

SIZE MATTERS!

Janet Van Dyne's amazing growth powers are thanks to a special size-altering molecule known as Pym Particles. Discovered by her husband Dr Hank Pym, these tiny atoms allow a person to shrink to just a few inches tall or grow to incredible heights.

TO BECOME A GIANT!

Originally, Jan fought super villains as the diminutive Wasp, alongside her husband who used Pym Particles to become Giant Man. But when her husband decided to retire from crime fighting to concentrate on his scientific studies, she took over his larger than life persona and became Giant Girl.

Using a special headset built into her mask, Giant Girl can control insects such as wasps or ants.

BATTLE TACTICS!

As Giant Girl grows in size her strength increases too. At full size she can lift up to an incredible 50 tons.

The maximum height Giant Girl can grow to is 100 feet. If she tried to become any taller it would put too much strain on her body and cause her to pass out.

Giant Girl can also use Pym Particles to change the size of other objects.

To draw you out we needed someone who could distract the guards. Ultron disabled the strength-dampening collar The Abomination wore and his cell's power field.

Voilà! Instant chaos.

"Ultron's Infiltrators hacked their way into your Quinjet's console--commandeering the guidance system and rigging the vents to disperse the same gas Dr. Banner is breathing now.

"While your performance kept all the guards enrapt, Ultron opened our cells. Of course, anyone watching the monitors would have seen footage of Zemo and me being model prisoners.

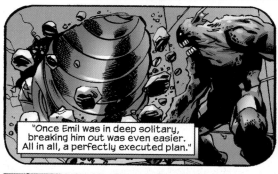

"Once Emil was in deep solitary, breaking him out was even easier. All in all, a perfectly executed plan."

HAS GLOATING CONCLUDED SUFFICIENTLY THAT SPIDER-MAN CAN BE DESTROYED?

Yes. Thanks for waiting.

So did that buy you enough time to figure a way out of here?

Gah! I got so caught up in the story, I forgot!

Go ahead, Ultron, blast away.

Wait!

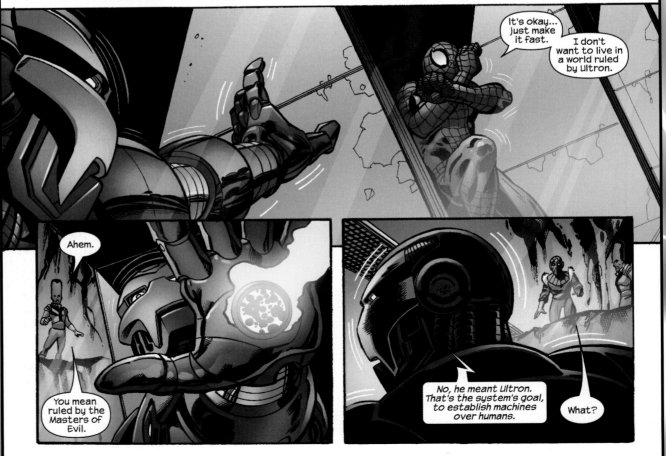

AVENGERS ROLLCALL!

FILE #06

Storm's eyes glow white when she uses her powers.

Her lightning bolts are powerful enough to take down a mutant-hunting Sentinel robot with one blast!

— STRANGE MUTATION! —

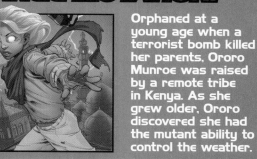

Orphaned at a young age when a terrorist bomb killed her parents, Ororo Munroe was raised by a remote tribe in Kenya. As she grew older, Ororo discovered she had the mutant ability to control the weather.

— TO BECOME A GODDESS! —

Due to her amazing powers, the people of her tribe worshipped her as a goddess. They would bring her gifts and treasures to ensure she would help them by creating rains for their crops or lightning to smite their enemies.

— THE ONCOMING STORM! —

Whilst seeking young mutants to form a new group of X-Men, Professor Charles Xavier journeyed to Kenya and offered Storm a place on his new team, which she accepted. Storm now serves as both an X-Man, saving young mutants from danger, and also as a member of the Avengers.

⚡ BATTLE TACTICS!

Along with her mutant abilities, Storm has an impressive knowledge of hand-to-hand combat, taught to her by her fellow team mate Wolverine.

Storm can fly by summoning winds to carry her through the air. Travelling this way she can reach a top speed of nearly 300 mph.

31

AVENGERS ACADEMY!

It takes more than just impressive powers to be a member of the Avengers. You also need a keen tactical mind and sharp wits -- apart from the Hulk of course, his huge fists more than make up for his lack of brains! See if you've got what it takes by solving these puzzles!

CAP CLONES!

Using an advanced holographic projector, Ultron has created five evil copies of Captain America. See if you can work out which is the real Cap by spotting the one who exactly matches the original!

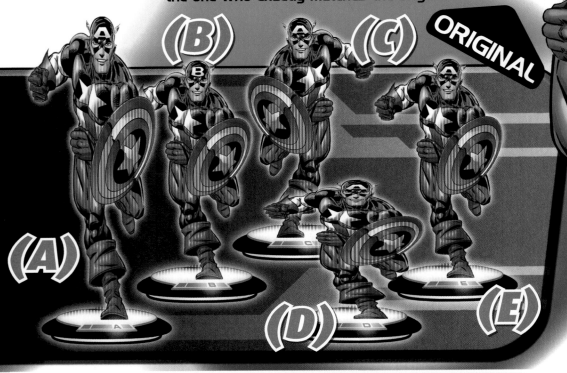

(A) (B) (C) (D) (E)

ORIGINAL

ANSWER

BOOK SMART!

Okay, it's time to see how much you really know about each of the Avengers. Take a look at these seven books from the Avengers library and see if you can match them up to the hero who would read them.

ANSWERS

1. Growing Pains by Ellie Vated
2. Animals of Africa by L.R. Phant
3. Controlling Rage by Anne Gree
4. Great Business Tips by Millie O'Nare
5. Shield Maintenance by V. I. Branium
6. Indestructible Metals by Adam Antium
7. Wall-Crawling for beginners by Honor Rooftop

PATH OF DESTRUCTION!

The Abomination is causing some serious property damage down town and the Hulk needs to get there fast! See if you can work out which route he should take to reach the gamma-powered goon!

START

FINISH

— ENEMY ALERT! —

"Listen up, troops, this is a priority 1 alert! A whole legion of super villains are invading the Avengers base and we need your help to stop them."

See if you can spot all their names in the word grid opposite!

Modoc

Ultron

Kang

Baron Zemo

Abomination

The Leader

Loki

Dr Doom

Magneto

Masters of Evil

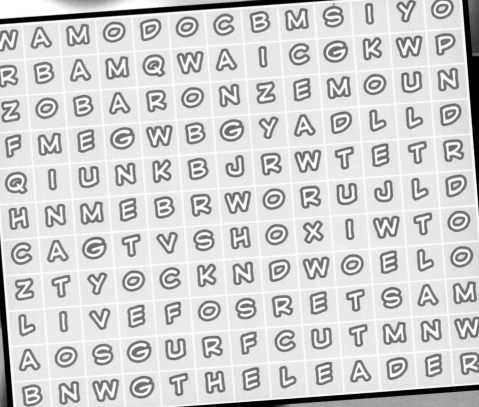

```
W A M O D O C B M S I Y O
R B A M Q W A I C G K W P
Z O B A R O N Z E M O U N
F M E G W B G Y A D L L D
Q I U N K B J R W T E T R
H N M E B R W O R U J L D
C A G T V S H O X I W T O
Z T Y O C K N D W O E L O
L I V E F O S R E T S A M
A O S G U R F C U T M N W
B N W G T H E L E A D E R
```

TURN TO PAGE 62 FOR THE ANSWERS.

33

A NOT-SO-BEAUTIFUL MIND

JEFF PARKER
WRITER

JUAN SANTACRUZ
PENCILS

RAUL FERNANDEZ
INKS

IMPACTO STUDIOS'
ADRIANO LUCAS
COLORS

DAVE SHARPE
LETTERS

CAMERON STEWART
and GURU eFX
COVER

BRAD JOHANSEN
PRODUCTION

NATHAN COSBY
ASST. EDITOR

MARK PANICCIA
EDITOR

JOE QUESADA
EDITOR IN CHIEF

DAN BUCKLEY
PUBLISHER

Captain America created by Joe Simon and Jack Kirby

THE MASTERS

ULTRON

Created by Dr Hank Pym, Ultron was supposed to be a peaceful mechanical servant. However, the rebellious robot turned against its creator and decided that instead of being a slave to humans, he should become their ruler! Luckily, the Avengers have always managed to foil his plans for world domination in the past, but they have never managed to stop him for good, due to his indestructible adamantium body.

His mechanical body is strong enough to lift over 15 tons.

Ultron can use a special weapon known as his 'Encephalo Beam' to hypnotise his opponents by broadcasting secret commands direct to their brains!

STRENGTH:	7
SPEED:	5
INTELLIGENCE:	9
AGILITY:	5
FIGHTING SKILL:	6

THE LEADER

Like the Hulk, the Leader gained his powers after being exposed to gamma radiation. However, instead of gaining incredible physical powers, he developed vast mental powers. With his gamma-enhanced brain, the Leader is one of the most cunning villains in the Marvel Universe. He prides himself on his quick wits and vast intellect, and believes he can outsmart any Super Hero.

He has low-level psychic powers, allowing him to control weak-minded people.

Due to the speed at which his brain processes information, The Leader can read over 4000 words a minute.

STRENGTH:	6
SPEED:	5
INTELLIGENCE:	10
AGILITY:	5
FIGHTING SKILL:	4

OF EVIL!

THE ABOMINATION

Bigger, stronger, smarter (and uglier) than the Hulk, the Abomination is a dangerous monster that thrives on chaos and destruction. He has all the Hulk's powers but at a much greater level, plus, unlike the good natured but dim-witted Hulk, he has a normal human level of intelligence. This combination of raw power and keen intellect makes him more than a match for even the toughest Super Heroes.

The Abomination's leg muscles are so strong he can easily leap up to a mile in one jump.

Unlike the Hulk, the Abomination does not get stronger as he gets angrier.

STRENGTH:	10
SPEED:	6
INTELLIGENCE:	7
AGILITY:	6
FIGHTING SKILL:	8

BARON ZEMO

The current Baron Zemo is the son of Baron Heinrich Zemo, a super villain who fought Captain America during World War 2. Zemo has made it his life's work to destroy Cap and the Avengers. Even though he has no super powers Zemo is a brilliant military strategist and expert at many forms of combat. He is also a scientific genius and has created many highly advanced weapons.

He has a vast knowledge of all military weapons and is a crack shot with rifles and pistols.

Baron Zemo never takes off his mask as his face was hideously scarred after falling into a boiling vat of an experimental compound known as Adhesive X.

STRENGTH:	5
SPEED:	4
INTELLIGENCE:	8
AGILITY:	7
FIGHTING SKILL:	10

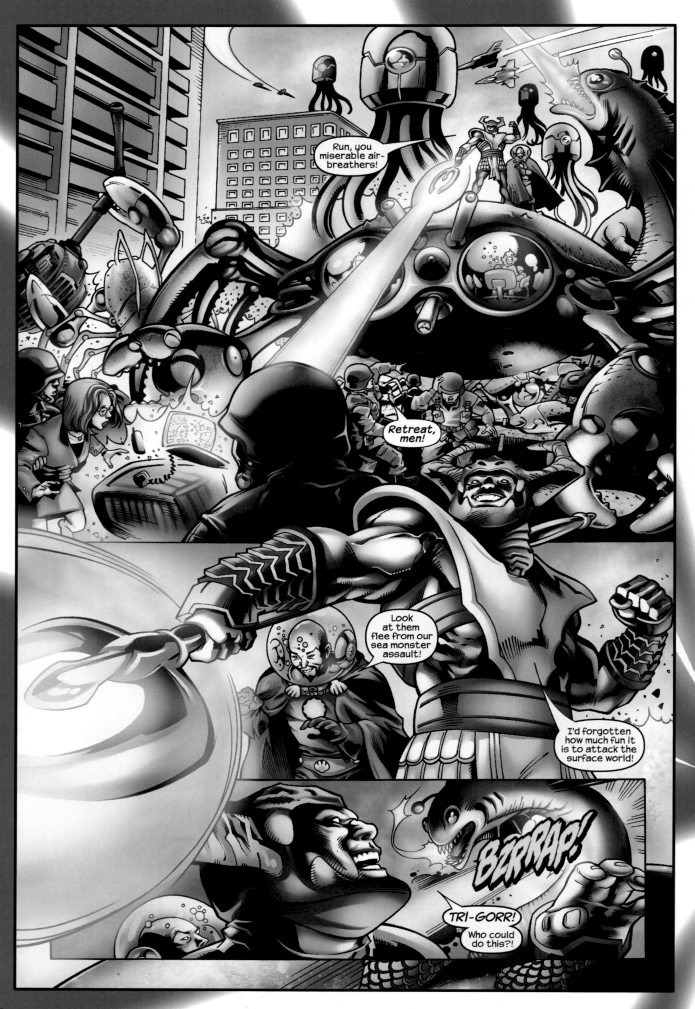

AVENGERS FILE #07 ROLLCALL!

HULK
This is one Super Hero you definitely don't want to get angry! Read on to discover all his secrets!

─ GAMMA GENESIS! ─

Whilst testing an experimental gamma bomb, timid scientist Dr Bruce Banner was accidentally caught in the blast as it detonated. Even though he was bathed in a huge dose of gamma radiation, Bruce appeared to have escaped the accident without any harm.

── GREEN RAGE! ──

However, the next time he got angry the bomb's effect on his body became apparent. His skin turned to a strange green colour and he suddenly grew to nearly three times his normal size. He had been transformed into the Hulk. A simple-minded creature who possessed an almost limitless level of strength and toughness.

── HUNTED! ──

For years he was hunted by the US military who saw him as a dangerous and unpredictable monster. But the Avengers realised he was a noble creature at heart and offered him a place on their team, knowing that both Dr Banner's scientific knowledge and the Hulk's strength would be valuable assets to their new team.

Thanks to the gamma radiation that flows through his body, the Hulk has a healing factor that allows him to regenerate from any injury.

⚡ BATTLE TACTICS!

As the Hulk gets angrier he also gets stronger. During one battle he became so enraged that he was able to pick up an entire mountain!

By slamming his mighty hands together, the Hulk can create a sonic boom capable of knocking even the sturdiest opponents off their feet.

CAPDOC

STORMDOC

SPIDOC

HULKDOC

GI-DOC

IRONDOC

WOLDOC

51

AVENGERS COLOUR ZONE!

Check it out guys! Prove you're a real Marvel maniac by grabbing your pens and pencils, and adding a splash of colour to the picture below!

52

AVENGERS BRAIN TEST!

1. A green skinned villain with a huge brain. (3,6)
2. This evil robot was created by Dr Hank Pym. (6)
3. AIM stands for Advanced Idea .... (9)
4. Spider-Man's girlfriend. (4, 4)
5. The Avengers' highly advanced flying craft. (7)
6. Captain America's shield is made of this rare metal. (9)
7. Giant Girl uses these to change her size. (3,9)
8. This super villain normally wears a purple outfit. (5,4)
9. Emil Blonsky's super villain alter ego. (11)
10. The type of radiation responsible for transforming Bruce Banner into the Hulk. (5)
11. Storm and Wolverine are also members of this team of mutants. (4)
12. Iron Man's real name is Tony ..... (5)

"I hope you've been reading all the fact files, cos it's time to test your knowledge of Marvel's most famous Super Heroes and villains with this cool super powered crossword. Good Luck!"

COLOUR GUIDE

TURN TO PAGE 62 FOR THE ANSWERS.

MODOC'S MIND BENDER!

PAY ATTENTION, YOU FEEBLE MINDED WORMS. I, MODOC, HAVE CREATED THIS TRICKY CONUNDRUM TO PROVE HOW STUPID NORMAL HUMANS REALLY ARE.

USING MY INCREDIBLE PSYCHIC SKILLS, I HAVE CREATED SEVEN FEINDISHLY DIFFICULT DIFFERENCES BETWEEN THESE TWO PICTURES, DO YOU THINK YOU CAN SPOT THEM ALL?

FOOLISH HUMANS! DO YOU REALLY THINK YOU'RE TEENY TINY BRAINS ARE A MATCH FOR MY COLOSSAL CRANIUM?

TURN TO PAGE 62 FOR THE ANSWERS.

ANSWERS

CAP CLONES!

CLONE (E) IS THE REAL CAP

BOOK SMART!

7 5 2 4
1 3 6

PATH OF DESTRUCTION!

— ENEMY ALERT! —

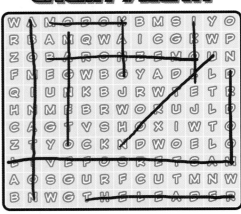

AVENGERS BRAIN TEST!

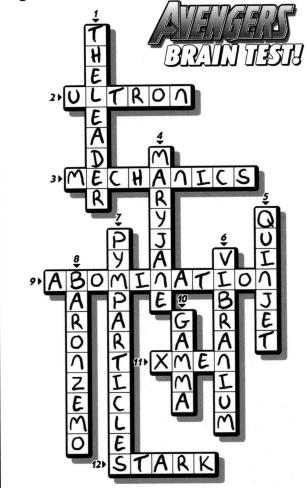

MODOC'S MIND BENDER!